Classical Highlights for Clarinet

Beliebte Klassiker für Clarinet

arranged for Clarinet and Piano
bearbeitet für Clarinet und Klavier

With piano accompaniment and play-along (pdf/mp3) for download
Mit Klavierbegleitung und Play-along (pdf/mp3) als Download

Edited by / Herausgegeben von
Kate Mitchell

ED 23449
ISMN 979-0-001-21373-8

Cover illustration:
Baroque ornament: © HiSunnySky – Fotolia.com
Photo of the instrument: Claudia Paulussen – Fotolia.com

T0050647

SCHOTT

www.schott-music.com

Mainz · London · Madrid · Paris · New York · Tokyo · Beijing

Inhalt / Contents

Bach, Johann Sebastian (1685–1750)
Air aus: Orchestersuite Nr. 3 D-Dur /
from: Orchestral Suite No. 3 D major, BWV 1068 . . . 3

Jesus bleibet meine Freude / Jesu, Joy of Man's Desiring
Choral aus der Kantate /
Chorale from the Cantata BWV 147 4

Händel, Georg Friedrich (1685–1759)
Largo aus der Oper / from the opera "Xerxes" . . . 6

Schubert, Franz (1797–1828)
Ave Maria op. 52/6 7

Mendelssohn, Felix (1809–1847)
Hochzeitsmarsch / Wedding March op. 61/9
aus: „Ein Sommernachtstraum" / from:
"A Midsummer Night's Dream" 8

Schumann, Robert (1810–1856)
Träumerei / Reveries op. 15/7 11

Wagner, Richard (1813–1883)
Treulich geführt – Brautchor aus /
Bridal Chorus from "Lohengrin" 12

Rubinstein, Anton (1829–1894)
Melodie / Melody op. 3/1 14

Johannes Brahms (1833–1897)
Ungarischer Tanz Nr. 5 /
Hungarian Dance No. 5 WoO 1/1 16

Fauré, Gabriel (1845–1914)
Après un rêve 18
Pavane op. 50 19

Fibich, Zdeněk (1850–1900)
Poème op. 39 22

Tárrega, Francisco (1852–1909)
Recuerdos de la Alhambra 23

Elgar, Edward (1857–1934)
Pomp and Circumstance – Military March No. 1 . . 24

MacDowell, Edward (1860–1908)
To a wild rose op. 51/1 28

Satie, Erik (1866–1925)
Gymnopédie No. 1 29

Ravel, Maurice (1875–1937)
Pavane pour une infante défunte 30

Kreisler, Fritz (1875–1962)
Liebesfreud – Liebesleid / Love's Joy – Love's Sorrow
aus: Alt-Wiener Tanzweisen /
from: Old Viennese Dance Tunes 32

Noack, Kurt (1895–1945)
Heinzelmännchens Wachtparade / Flibbertigibbets . 38

Pütz, Eduard (1911–2000)
Blue Waltz 40

Auf der Website **www.schott-music.com/online-material** können alle Audio-Dateien mit dem folgenden Gutscheincode kostenlos heruntergeladen werden: **txkZE4f7**

Please visit **www.schott-music.com/online-material** to download all audio files for free using the following voucher code: **txkZE4f7**

Die Klavierbegleitungen können auf der Website **www.schott-music.com/webcodes** mit folgendem Code heruntergeladen werden: **L8YXxrwt**

To download the piano accompaniment please visit **www.schott-music.com/webcodes** using the following voucher code: **L8YXxrwt**

Track 1

Air

aus der Orchestersuite Nr. 3 D-Dur
from the Orchestral Suite No. 3 D major
BWV 1068

Arr.: Wolfgang Birtel

Johann Sebastian Bach
1685–1750

Track 2

Jesus bleibet meine Freude

Jesu, Joy of Man's Desiring

Arr.: Wolfgang Birtel

Johann Sebastian Bach
1685–1750

aus der Kantate „Herz und Mund und Tat und Leben" / from the Cantata "Heart and Mouth and Deed and Life", BWV 147

36
39
42
45
49
53
(tr)
1
59
(tr)
63
66
69

Track 3

Largo

aus der Oper / from the opera »Xerxes«

Arr.: Wolfgang Birtel

Georg Friedrich Händel
1685–1759

Track 4

Ave Maria

opus 52/6

Arr.: Rudolf Mauz

Franz Schubert
1797–1828

Molto adagio, religioso

Track 5

Hochzeitsmarsch
aus »Ein Sommernachtstraum«
Wedding March
from »A Midsummer Night s Dream«
opus 61/9

Arr.: Wolfgang Birtel

Felix Mendelssohn
1809–1847

30
sf
sf
34
1.
2.
sf
36
sf
sf
40
1.
2.
sf
44
ff
tr
48
tr
p
59
64
p
69
1
sf
dim.
p

75
mf
molto cresc.
82
cresc.
p cresc.
89
ff
tr
95
101
107
113
119
125
1.
2.
130

Track 6

Träumerei
Reveries
opus 15/7

Arr.: Wolfgang Birtel

Robert Schumann
1810–1856

aus: „Kinderszenen“ / from: “Scenes of Childhood“

Track 7

Treulich geführt

Brautchor aus / Bridal Chorus from »Lohengrin«

Arr.: Wolfgang Birtel

Richard Wagner
1813–1883

-de Tempo primo

Track 8

Melodie
Melody
opus 3/1

Arr.: Wolfgang Birtel

Anton Rubinstein
1829–1894

65
a tempo
poco rit.
a tempo
75
mf dolce e espress.
85
1
f
94
poco rit.
a tempo
p
rit.
103
pp
a tempo
mp
poco rit.
113
a tempo
mf
f
123
p
134
rit.
p
pp
3
3
mf
pp

Track 9

Ungarischer Tanz Nr. 5

Hungarian Dance No. 5

WoO 1/1

Arr.: Rudolf Mauz

Johannes Brahms
1833–1897

49
Vivace
sf
sf
sf
58
sf
poco rit.
p
a tempo
legg.
poco rit.
a tempo
68
poco rit.
a tempo
poco rit.
a tempo
77
Allegro
f fieramente
88
p legg.
sf
f
sf
96
sf
poco rit.
p
104
a tempo
sf
sf
5
ff

Track 10

Après un rêve

Arr.: Wolfgang Birtel

Gabriel Fauré
1845–1924

Track 11

Pavane

opus 50

Arr.: Wolfgang Birtel

Gabriel Fauré
1845–1914

Andante molto moderato (♩ = 84)

47
ff
2
ff
52
mf
ff
56
mf
59
p
3
63
1
p
3
3
f
(tr
68
(tr)
)
p
73
f
p

77
81
f
85
89
p espress.
mf
p
pp
93
p
97
tranquillement
101
f *pp*

Track 12

Poème
opus 39

Arr.: Wolfgang Birtel

Zdeněk Fibich
1850–1900

aus der Idylle „Am Abend“ / from the Idyll “At Twilight”

Track 13

Arr.: Wolfgang Birtel

Recuerdos de la Alhambra

Francisco Tárrega
1852–1909

Andante

Track 14

Pomp and Circumstance

Military March No. 1

opus 39/1

Arr.: Wolfgang Birtel

Edward Elgar
1857–1934

cresc. poco a poco
poco
pesante
allargando
TRIO. Largamente
legato e cantabile
allargando
a tempo
espress.
dim.
Molto maestoso
allargando
a tempo
espress.

Tempo primo
157
f
simile
163
sf
168
sf
mf
5
animato
173
molto cresc.
ff
179
ten.
a tempo
186
ten.
1
sf
sf
192
sf
sf
p
f
196
cresc. poco a poco
203
ff

211
sf
216
poco allargando
pesante
222
Molto maestoso
ff
simile
232
239
247
allargando
ad lib. 8
255
rit.
(8)
Tempo primo
264
Più mosso
270

Track 15

To a wild rose

opus 51/1

Arr.: Wolfgang Birtel

Edward MacDowell
1860–1908

aus „Amerikanische Wald-Idyllen“ / from “Woodland Sketches”

Track 16

Gymnopédie No. 1

Arr.: Wolfgang Birtel

Erik Satie
1866–1925

Lent et douloureux

Track 17

Pavane
pour une infante défunte

Arr.: Wolfgang Birtel

Maurice Ravel
1875–1937

Très grave
ad lib.
pp fugace
Flz. (ad lib.)
Très grave
Au Mouvement
cédez
Au Mouvement
en élargissant beaucoup
perdendosi

Track 18

Liebesfreud

Love's Joy

Arr.: Wolfgang Birtel

Fritz Kreisler
1875–1962

aus: Alt-Wiener Tanzweisen, Nr. 1 / from: Old Viennese Dance Tunes, No. 1

52
58
65
a tempo
tr
p
f
70
tr
f
76
p
p grazioso
81
90
97
106
rit.
p

a tempo
1.
2.

Track 19

Liebesleid
Love’s Sorrow

Arr.: Wolfgang Birtel

Fritz Kreisler

Tempo di Ländler

aus: Alt-Wiener Tanzweisen, Nr. 2 / from: Old Viennese Dance Tunes, No. 2

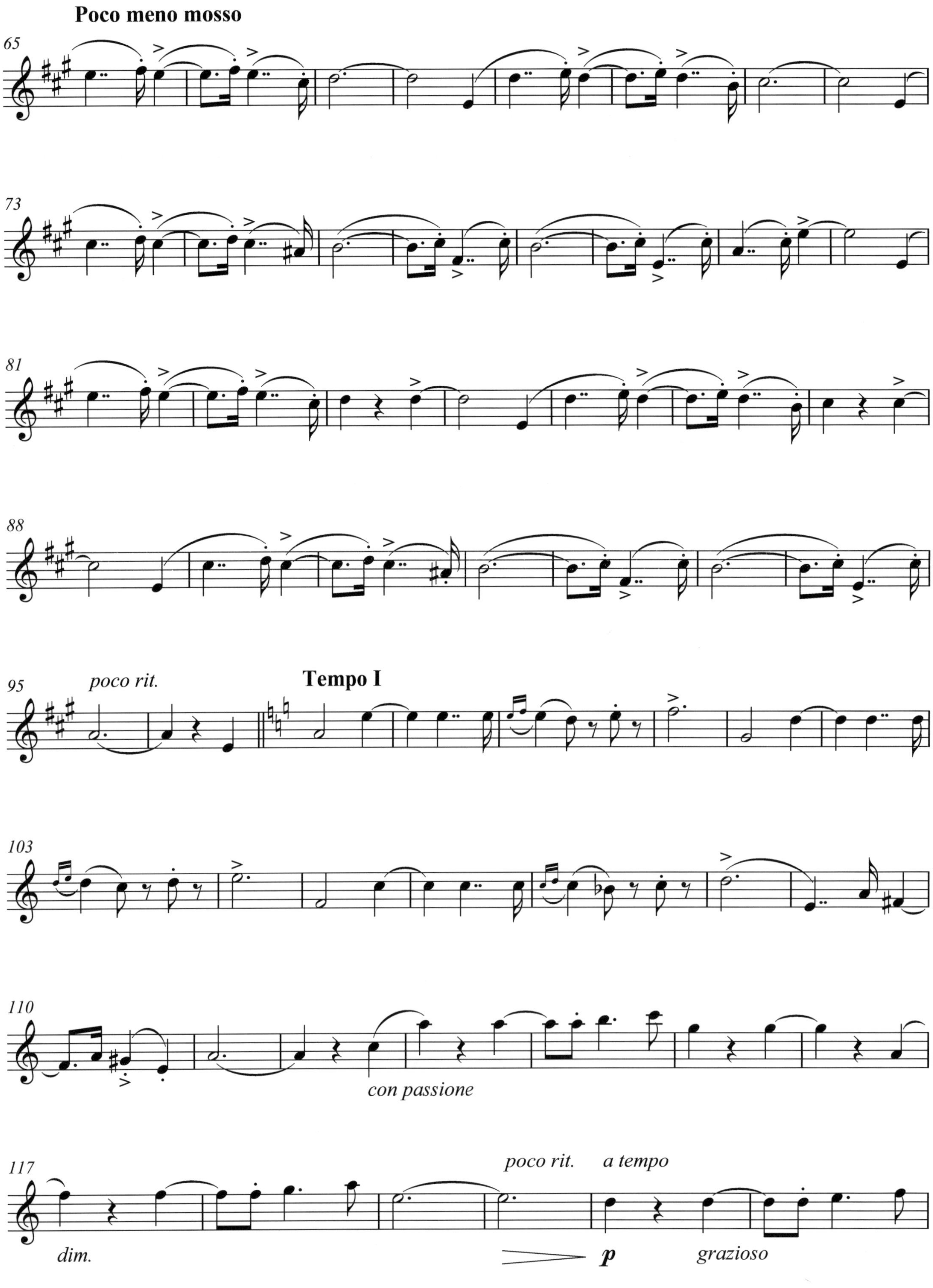
Poco meno mosso
65
73
81
88
95
poco rit.
Tempo I
103
110
con passione
117
dim.
poco rit.
a tempo
p
grazioso

123
Poco meno mosso
129
pp
135
142
149
155
tr
161
p
perdendosi

Track 20

Heinzelmännchens Wachtparade

Flibbertigibbets

Opus 5

Arr.: Wolfgang Birtel

Kurt Noack
1895–1945

D. S. al Fine,
poi Trio
Trio
1. pp 2. ff e più lento

Track 21

Blue Waltz

Arr.: Wolfgang Birtel

Eduard Pütz
1911–2000